Hanging by a Fred

John Townsend

Stanley Thornes (Publishers) Ltd

Originally published in 1986 by Hutchinson Education

Reprinted in 1990 by
Stanley Thornes (Publishers) Ltd
Ellenborough House
Wellington Street
CHELTENHAM GL50 1YW

00 / 10 9 8

British Library Cataloguing in Publication Data

Townsend, John, *1924–*
    Hanging by a Fred. — (Spirals).
    1. Readers
    I. Title   II. Series
    428.6'2   PE1119

ISBN 0 7487 0357 8

Cover illustration by Simon Rees, cover design by Ned Hoste

Set in Linotron 202 Rockwell
Printed and bound in Great Britain by
Martin's The Printers, Berwick.

Contents

Hanging by a Fred

A play for ten parts (and parcels!)

Jackson, lift attendant
Mrs Gladys Peak
Mr Gordon Peak, her husband
Old lady
Amanda, a nurse
Frederick, her ex-boyfriend
Manager, Mr Stradling
Santa Claus, a crook
Store detective
Cleaner

The play is set in a lift on Christmas Eve in Stradling's department store. All characters carry carrier bags which all look exactly the same!

Scene 1 Ground floor.

Jackson	Going up. Going up.
Mrs Peak	Ah, the lift! Quick, quick, you've got to get me up to the fifth floor – hurry.
Jackson	All in good time, madam. Next floor for furniture, fittings and hardware. Going up. Going up.

7

Mrs Peak	Get a move on. I've left my husband up in the café on the fifth floor. I thought he'd come down the other stairs.
Jackson	Going up for kitchen fittings, beds, hardware . . . .
Mrs Peak	I don't know what he's playing at. 'Meet me in ladies' tights' I told him. I only hope he's got our shopping. Just wait till I get hold of him.
Jackson	Going up to the first floor.
Mrs Peak	No, no – I told you, you've got to go straight to the top – hurry. This bag is not mine. I grabbed the wrong parcel.
Jackson	Anyone else for the first floor?
Mrs Peak	You're being plain awkward, aren't you?
Jackson	It's my job, madam.
Mrs Peak	I knew it was a mistake to come shopping on Christmas Eve.
Jackson	Going up, going up . . . . Wallpaper, dining room chairs . . . .
	[Old lady *enters*]
Old lady	Plugs?

8

Jackson	Yes, madam, next floor for furniture and fittings.
Mrs Peak	Will you hurry up? I need to go straight to the top.
Jackson	I stop at every floor, madam.
Mrs Peak	You can be awkward, you know. I'll leave the bag right here and you can sort it out. I'll take the stairs. [*She storms out*]
Jackson	Not in MY lift you don't. [*He puts the bag outside*] Going up. Going up, mind the doors, going up.

[*Doors close*]

Old lady	Ooo er . . . can't you slow this lift down a bit? I've gone all funny. I don't know how you can stand this job.
Jackson	Oh, it has its ups and downs, madam.
Old lady	You must get dizzy.
Jackson	I get used to it. It's a very exciting job. I've always wanted to travel in my work. It's a good way to get on in life – to start at the bottom and work up!
Old lady	But isn't it badly paid and boring?

| Jackson | Not at all. I often get a rise! If I'm feeling down in the dumps, I simply press the button and I'm up in the air, on top of the world and high as a kite – well, as high as the café on the fifth floor! Oh, here we are. It's the first floor, madam. |

Jackson   Not at all. I often get a rise! If I'm feeling down in the dumps, I simply press the button and I'm up in the air, on top of the world and high as a kite – well, as high as the café on the fifth floor! Oh, here we are. It's the first floor, madam.

Old lady   Well, I only hope I can get my plugs here. I need them for Christmas. It's vital. [*Doors open*] I'll leave my bag out here . . . .
[*She exits*]

Scene 2   First floor

Jackson   Going up. Going up. Next floor for menswear, shoes, trousers, suits . . . .

[Mr Peak *enters, carrying a bag*]

Mr Peak   Top floor, please.

Jackson   All in good time, sir. Shirts, ties, socks . . . .

Mr Peak   Only I've lost the wife, you see. She'll be mad if she can't find me. I dread to think.

Jackson   Going up for umbrellas, hats, coats, scarves . . . .

Mr Peak   I just had time to nip off and buy her present and when I came back, she'd gone

– not a sign of her in ladies' tights! So I bought her some perfume. It cost a fortune but worth every penny to keep her happy!

Jackson   Going up for sports clothes, beach wear, all on the next floor.

[Amanda, *a nurse, enters*]

Amanda   Third floor, please – it's an emergency.

Jackson   You'll have to wait your turn, miss. All in good time.

Amanda   But there's been an accident with a washing machine.

Mr Peak   Oh dear. What on earth happened?

Amanda   In the middle of the hot wash, it turned some trousers inside out, melted the braces and scorched a hole in the seat.

Mr Peak   But what's that got to do with you? You're a nurse.

Amanda   The salesman was wearing them at the time!

[Frederick *enters*]

Frederick   Oh – it's you – Amanda!

Amanda   Frederick – how could you?

11

Frederick	Oh don't say that, Amanda. You know I've been true to you.
Jackson	Mind the doors. Going up.

[*Doors close*]

Amanda	How can you say that, Frederick? You lied to me.
Mr Peak	It's been pretty mild for December, hasn't it?
Frederick	Oh Amanda! Oh Amanda! Oh Amanda!
Jackson	They say there'll be a frost tonight, though.
Amanda	Frederick, how can you mean that after what you said?
Frederick	But I bought you these as a present to say 'sorry'. They're in this bag – roses. You'll like them, they weren't cheap. I thought I'd say it with flowers.
Amanda	Huh! I like that! I don't need to say it with flowers, words will do – CLEAR OFF!
Mr Peak	Let's hope it doesn't rain then.
Frederick	Oh Amanda – please give me another chance – please!
Amanda	How dare you say that to me. How have you got the nerve, you slimy toad. You

horrid brute, you . . . .

Jackson   Snow would be nice for Christmas.

Frederick   Are you trying to tell me something, Amanda?

Amanda   I thought I'd said it.   I hate the sight of you.   You pig.

Mr Peak   We haven't had a white Christmas for years.

Frederick   You don't mean that.   You *can't* mean that.

Mr Peak   Oh yes I do.   It's quite true.

Amanda   Yes I do.   I hate you.   I loathe you.   I detest the thought of you.   I feel sick at the thought of the air you breathe and the ground you walk on.

Frederick   It's nothing personal then?

Jackson   I think four years ago we did.

Amanda   Shut up!   Besides, there's someone else in my life now.

Mr Peak   So we did.

Frederick   There's someone else?   Who, Amanda? Tell me who.

Amanda   Rodney.   I've fallen for somebody else.

[*Doors open*]

Scene 3   Second floor

Jackson   Second floor for menswear . . . .

Amanda   So you can keep your rotten parcel of roses
               and greenfly, and my bag for that matter.
               I'll get to the next floor by the stairs.   You
               can leave the stupid parcels in here for all
               I care. [*She storms off, throwing down
               bags*]

Frederick   I wonder if she meant what she said.   I'd
               better leave her bag out here.   [*He puts it
               out on the landing*]

Mr Peak   Well I'll just pop out here while we've
               stopped and look for the wife – just in
               case.   I'll leave her present in here if I
               may, I don't want her to see me with it.
               [*He exits*]

Jackson   Not in MY lift you don't.   [*He puts it
               outside*]

Frederick   I'll hang on to my roses. They're all I've
               got left in the world . . .

Jackson   Next floor – the third floor – for electrical
               goods . . . televisions, radios, videos,
               computers, records, tapes . . .

Frederick   I think I'll go straight to the top – and jump
               off.

14

Jackson	... toasters ... floppy discs ... dish washers ... clocks ....
Frederick	Yes – I'm going to do myself in.

[Old lady *enters*]

Old lady	Oh good, caught you again. I need the third floor now.
Jackson	How did you get up here so quickly?

[*Doors close*]

Old lady	Simple. I ran. I still need those plugs. It's vital. Oh dear, my bag's still downstairs. Can you take me back?
Jackson	Certainly not. It's strictly against the rules for me to go down when I've said I'm going up.
Old lady	I see this young man has a parcel just like mine.
Frederick	Roses. I thought I'd say it with flowers. I failed.
Old lady	How sad – oooh, this lift gives me the colly-wobbles.
Frederick	I don't want them any more. You can have them if you like.

15

Old lady	Super! Where can I put them? I'll leave them in here.
Jackson	Not in MY lift you don't. Just leave them on the landing on the third floor. We're here now.

[*Doors open*]

Scene 4 Third floor

Old lady	Oh good, perhaps they'll have my plugs. [*She exits with roses*]
Jackson	Third floor for electrical goods. Going up to Santa.

[Manager *enters*]

Manager	How do you do, Jackson. Next floor, please.
Jackson	Very well, sir. Yes, sir, Mr Stradling, sir.

[Mrs Peak *enters*]

Mrs Peak	Gordon? Gordon? Ah, the lift again. I've been running up all those stairs. I'm worn out. I'll have to use the lift.
Manager	Get a move on then, Jackson.

16

Jackson	Very well, sir. Going up. Going up.
Mrs Peak	I've just made it then. Fourth floor for me.

[*Doors close*]

Manager	Hurry up about it, Jackson. Today's pretty hectic, you know. This bag I've got is full of fivers so I've got to get them in the safe, eh? The thing is, I've just got to hop out for a sec at the next floor but I'll be right back so you can take me up to the office at the top. Just keep this bag by you while I jump out, eh?
Jackson	Not in MY ... er certainly, sir.
Mrs Peak	I can't think what's happened to Gordon. There'll be trouble, mark my words.
Frederick	I'm going to end it all.
Mrs Peak	Lucky you. I've still got lots to buy yet.
Manager	[*Whispering*] Now remember, Jackson, keep that beady eye of yours on those fivers, eh? It could mean a little Christmas bonus for you, what?

[*Doors open*]

Scene 5 Fourth floor

Jackson	Fourth floor. Toys and Santa's Grotto.
Manager	I won't be a min. Hold on to the bag. [*He exits*]
Mrs Peak	If he's not on this floor, there'll be hell to pay. [*She exits*]
Frederick	I could always plunge down the lift shaft.

[Santa *enters, barging in with sack and in a panic. He presses button*]

Santa	Quick – get me out of here.

[*Doors close*]

Jackson	Hey! You can't do that. [*He presses button – doors open*]
Santa	Want to bet? [*He presses button – doors close*]
Jackson	Now look here – just who do you think you are?
Santa	[*Pressing button – doors close*] Well if you can't guess who I am dressed like this, here's a clue: Ho, ho, ho! Merry Christmas!
Jackson	Now look what you've done. We're going down. This is not allowed. I forbid it ....
Frederick	... unless I throw myself in the river ...

18

Jackson	It is strictly against the rules. I'm not letting you out at the next floor. I'm in charge of my lift.
Santa	Want to bet?
Jackson	Certainly.
Santa	See my bag? This package in my hot little hand ...
Jackson	You can't brush me off with all this Father Christmas presents rubbish ...
Santa	It's a bomb.
Jackson	Blimey!
Frederick	Help! Let me out! I don't want to die – not just yet!
Jackson	But I've got all Mr Stradling's fivers. He'll be cross.
	[*Doors open*]

Scene 6 Third floor

Santa	Oh good! Then let me help you out. [*He snatches the bag and runs off*]
Jackson	Come back! He can't do that!
Frederick	He just has – and taken his bomb with him.

Jackson	Right – I'll report him for that. Back to the manager. Going up – and quick about it . . . .

[Mr Peak *enters*]

Mr Peak	Oh jolly good – here you are. No sign of the wife, er . . . .
Jackson	Quick – get in – we're going up.

[Amanda *enters*]

Amanda	False alarm – fourth floor, please.
Frederick	Oh, Amanda!
Amanda	Not you again.
Jackson	Going up – quick – emergency.

[*Doors close*]

Mr Peak	Hey – wait a minute, I've left my parcel downstairs.
Amanda	And what have you done with my bag?
Jackson	More important – what about Mr Stradling's fivers?
Frederick	Oh I'm sorry Amanda.
Amanda	Leave me alone, I've told you what I feel.

20

Mr Peak	What am I going to do?
Jackson	What am I going to do?
Frederick	What am I going to do?
Amanda	Get knotted!
Frederick	Right – I will. I'll tie a knot in a rope and hang myself.
Amanda	And I couldn't care less. Now let me out of this lift before I go mad.

[*Doors open – she exits*]

Scene 7 Fourth floor

Jackson	Fourth floor for children's games, toys, Santa's Grotto – no Santa, just the grotto . . . .
Mr Peak	I'd better get out here and look for the wife. [*He exits*]

[Store detective *enters*]

Detective	Quick – after him.
Frederick	Who?
Detective	Father Christmas. Which way did he go?
Jackson	Down. Why?

Detective	He's a crook. I'm the store detective. I caught him red-handed. He ran off with masses of diamonds.
Frederick	He said it was a bomb he was carrying.
Detective	And diamonds. He had two bags in his sack. Look, can I leave this bag in here while I dash off and catch the blighter?
Jackson	Not in MY lift you don't.
Detective	But it's full of top secret papers.
Jackson	Then you'll have to leave it out there on the landing like everyone else has to.
Detective	Look, I can't stand around here all day. That Father Christmas is a thief. Now hurry up and get down there after him. [*S/he presses button – doors close*]
Jackson	Now just a moment – that's my job. [*He presses button – doors open*]
Detective	I command you to obey. [*S/he presses button – doors close*]
Jackson	Now stop messing about with my button. [*He presses button – doors open*]

[Mrs Peak *enters*]

Mrs Peak	Oh good. I've just caught you. Have you

seen my husband? He's really getting me cross now.

Detective Close the doors or I'll have you arrested for getting in the way of the law. [*S/he presses button – doors close*]

Frederick All this opening and closing could blow a fuse.

Detective I will blow a fuse in a minute.

Mrs Peak So will I. Where is the man?

Jackson So will I. Now open this door [*He presses button – doors open*] You great big steaming ... oh hello, Mr Stradling.

Manager Jolly good, Jackson. Everything all right?

Mrs Peak No – I want my husband.

Jackson Er um fine, sir. Going down! [*He presses button – doors close*]

Manager There seems to be a problem.

Mrs Peak Yes – I've lost my husband and it's Christmas.

Frederick I've lost Amanda and it's terrible.

Detective I've lost Santa and it's urgent.

Manager I'm not sure I follow this. So long as you haven't lost anything, Jackson. Wait a minute – why are we going down?

23

Jackson	Well it's like this, sir . . .
Manager	Something wrong? Well what have you got to say, Jackson?
Jackson	Third floor! Electrical goods, televisions, videos, radios, tapes, records . . . going up.

[*Doors open*]

Scene 8 Third floor

Detective	I'm going – and I'll take my parcel after all. [*He exits*]
Mrs Peak	I'm off and when I find him, I'll give him a jolly good piece of my mind. [*She exits*]
Frederick	I suppose I could always stab myself to death.
Manager	Jackson – what has happened to my fivers?
Jackson	Oh well, sir, you see it was like this . . . .
Frederick	Unless I try poison.

[Old lady enters]

Old lady	Oh good – caught you again. I still can't get my plugs. I'd better try the next floor. Are you going up?

Manager	Oh yes, we're going up all right – to my office, Jackson, for a little chat. I'm going to say a little word in your ear.
	[*Doors close*]
Jackson	And what word would that be, sir?
Manager	FIVERS – where are they?
Jackson	Santa has your money, sir.
Manager	Is this some kind of joke? Then I'll stop off at the next floor and tell Santa just what I want.
Old lady	Aren't you a bit old for that kind of thing? By the way, I can't remember where I left my bag.
Jackson	It's on the first floor landing, madam. It'll be quite safe there, you know.
Old lady	Not if they get hungry.
Jackson	Pardon?
Old lady	My snakes. They're in my bag. I take them everywhere with me. They're my pets.
Jackson	Blimey – and you've left them all alone?
Old lady	Oh don't worry about them being alone – they've got each other for company.

Jackson	Are they ... deadly?
Old lady	Oh no – well, only if somebody touches them.
Frederick	Just what I'm looking for!
Manager	What's up? Not more trouble, Jackson?
Jackson	Well, sir, apart from Santa running off with all the store's diamonds and your fivers, clutching a bomb, there are deadly snakes on the loose on the first floor. That's all, sir.
Manager	Snakes on the first floor? Nonsense, if I remember rightly, that's household furniture and fittings. Snakes would more likely be on the third or fourth .... Did you say SNAKES? Let me out immediately!

[*Doors open – he exits*] |

Scene 9 Fourth floor

Old lady	I'd better try here for my plugs. Can I leave my bag of roses with you for a minute?
Jackson	Not in MY lift you don't. Take it with you. [*She exits as* Mr Peak *enters*]
Mr Peak	No sign of her here – I'd better go up a

floor. I see you're still here, young man. Have you cheered up?

Frederick   No. I'm so depressed I'm going to kill myself twice.

Jackson   Going up. Going up to the fifth floor.

[*Doors close*]

Mr Peak   Did you say 'kill yourself'?

Frederick   It's the only way out.

Mr Peak   Don't let a woman upset you. If I were to do that, I would have shot myself every Christmas for the past thirty years.

Frederick   I've made up my mind. I will jump from the roof.

Mr Peak   Look, how about a nice cup of tea first. There's a café at this next floor – I'll treat you. How's that?

Jackson   Fifth floor coming up, gentlemen.

Frederick   I suppose I could throw myself under a bus . . . .

Jackson   Fifth floor for café, tea room and restaurant . . . .

[*Doors open*]

Scene 10 Fifth floor

[Cleaner *barges in*]

Cleaner Nobody leave this lift.

Jackson Now look here.

Cleaner I've lost it and I'm going to get it back. [*S/ he presses button*]

Jackson Not in MY lift you don't. That is my button. Only I can press it. [*He presses button*]

Cleaner Hard luck. We're going down because I said so. I'm the cleaner round here, so there.
[*S/he presses button*]

Jackson What is all this about?

[*Doors close*]

Cleaner Rats. Disease. I found them in the drains. This whole place could be infested. Nobody move. We're going down.

Frederick Let me out.

Mr Peak But we've just come up from the fourth floor.

Cleaner	Sorry but it's my job. That dead rat was going for tests but someone swiped it. It went.
Jackson	Went? A dead rat? Went?
Cleaner	Gone.
Frederick	Gone?
Cleaner	Pinched.
Mr Peak	Pinched?
Cleaner	Pinched. I put it down in a bag next to some bossy old woman in the tea queue and it went. I've got her shopping here and she's got my rat.
Mr Peak	That was my wife.
Cleaner	No – it was definitely a rat.
Mr Peak	It was Gladys.
Cleaner	I don't care what it was called, it was a dirty, smelly dead rat. A health hazard – upside down in the fairy cakes.
	[*Doors open*]

Scene 11 Fourth floor

Jackson	Going down.

[Manager *enters*]

Manager   Ah – here you are. Going down? I want to go up.

Cleaner   Well you can't.

Manager   Just a minute – who's the boss round here? Who keeps this place going? Who is the most important person in this whole building?

Cleaner   Me. I clean the place.

[Old lady *enters*]

Old lady   It's no good, I can't get those plugs anywhere.

[Amanda *enters*]

Amanda   I want the ground floor.

Frederick   Amanda – it's you again!

Amanda   Push off. I don't want to speak to you ever again.

Jackson   Going down.

[*Doors close*]

Manager   Now look, I'm not happy about all this.

Cleaner	Just as soon as I get my rat back I'll be quite happy.
Old lady	Did you say 'rat'? How wonderful.
Cleaner	Why, do you like rats or something?
Old lady	No – but my snakes do.
Frederick	[*whispering*] Amanda, we must speak.
Amanda	I've already told you. You disgust me.
Frederick	But don't let a little thing like that spoil our friendship.
Old lady	If you're the manager, I've got a complaint.
Manager	Oh really?
Old lady	I've spent all day searching this place for plugs. I can't find any.
Manager	Simple. First floor – household items – bathroom plugs.
Old lady	Not that sort of plug.
Manager	Oh easy. Third floor for electrical plugs.
Old lady	Not that sort of plug.
Manager	Then try the ground floor and ask for ear plugs.
Old lady	Not that sort of plug.
Manager	Then what sort do you want?

Old lady	Spark plugs, of course – for my motorbike. I need them urgently for the Hells Angels' Rally on Boxing Day.
Jackson	Ah! Here we are – the third floor.

[*Doors open*]

Scene 12 Third floor

Jackson	Electrical goods ... TVs ... videos ... radios ....
Mr Peak	Oh my word, there's the wife!

[Mrs Peak *enters*]

Mrs Peak	Why there you are, you stupid man. Where have you been? Have you got our shopping back? I've been looking everywhere for you. What have you got to say for yourself?
Mr Peak	How nice to see you again, dear.
Mrs Peak	I'll have a lot to say when I get you home.

[Store detective *enters*]

Detective	Quick – he's gone up the stairs to the fourth floor. After him! [*S/he presses button*]

Cleaner	You can't do that, I want to go down. [*S/he presses button*]
Manager	No, we've got to get my fivers back. Up it is. [*He presses button*]
Cleaner	I don't think so. I need that rat. [*S/he presses button*]
Mrs Peak	Stop all this. I need a cup of tea. We're all going up so you'll like it or lump it. [*She presses button*]
Jackson	I'm feeling left out of this. Going down. [*He presses button*]
Frederick	Please speak to me, Amanda or I'll kill myself here and now.
Jackson	Not in MY lift you don't.
Manager	We are going UP! [*He presses button – doors close*]
Mr Peak	It's very hot in here.
Mrs Peak	Be quiet and get your wallet ready.
Detective	Can't this lift go any faster? I've been chasing him all through the store. He's been gathering parcels on his way – on all the landings. He's a real crook.
Old lady	Who?
Detective	Santa. He even grabbed a package from

the first floor landing.

Old lady   My snakes!

Detective   Then another from the second floor.

Amanda   My first aid kit!

Cleaner   And somebody took my bag from the fifth
            floor.

Mrs Peak   And somebody took MY bag from the fifth
            floor.

Cleaner   Then it is you who's got it!

Mrs Peak   And you've got mine.

            [*They swap bags*]

Mr Peak   Thank goodness for that.

Jackson   Here we are – fourth floor for Santa's
            Grotto.

Scene 13   Fourth floor

            [*Doors open and* Santa leaps in with big
            sack]

Santa   This is a hijack. Take this lift to the
            ground floor. [*He presses button*]

Mrs Peak	Oh no you don't. I want to go up. [*She presses button*]
Santa	Down. [*He presses button*]
Manager	Up. [*He presses button*]
Cleaner	Down. [*S/he presses button*]
Frederick	Up. [*He presses button*]
Amanda	Down. [*She presses button*]
Mr Peak	Up. [*He presses button*]
Old lady	Down. [*She presses button*]
Jackson	Up. [*He presses button*]
Detective	Stop! This man is under arrest. [*S/he presses button*] Santa – Mr S. Claus, the game is up. Anything you say will be taken down.
Santa	The lift! [*He presses button*]
Mr Peak	What's that burning smell?

[*Doors close*]

Jackson	The fuses. The wires are heating. The button is red hot.
Cleaner	We've broken something.

Old lady	Ooer . . . eeh! I feel all funny. Something's happening.
Frederick	We're shaking. We're all going to die!
	[*Everyone shakes, sways, jumps then falls to the floor*]
Santa	Let me out of here. We're going to crash. [*All scream*]
Detective	[*Grabbing* Santa's *leg*] You won't get away with it.
Jackson	Nobody move. The lift is stuck – we've jammed.
Mr Peak	How high up are we?
Manager	Nobody panic. Help! Help! HELP!
Cleaner	We're four floors up, plus the basement, plus the underground car park – then the sewers.
Frederick	That's a long way to fall. It'll kill the lot of us.
Amanda	This is a nightmare.
Old lady	This seems awfully serious – how exciting!
Mrs Peak	Gordon, if we get killed, I shall be furious.
Mr Peak	Yes, dear.

Mrs Peak	I shall have some very strong words to say on the matter. All that shopping will be ruined – wasted.
Mr Peak	Yes, dear.
Mrs Peak	And that turkey will go off, the pudding will spoil and what about the mince pies I left in the oven – and goodness knows what mess the cat will make in the sun-lounge – and it's all your fault!

[*They all squeal as they roll to one side*]

Manager	Santa, I blame you for all this – you're fired. You've now got the sack.
Detective	Yes, and it's full of parcels – all stolen.
Santa	And I mean to keep them all – so there!
Old lady	What a nasty Father Christmas. Times have certainly changed since I was a girl. Are you being a rascal, young man?
Santa	Clear off, granny.
Old lady	How dare you. No one gets away with that. [*She gives Santa a left hook on the nose*]
Frederick	Don't rock the lift – it won't take the strain.
Santa	Aaah, blimey, now look what you've

done. I've got a nose bleed now.

Old lady Serves you right.

Frederick Blood! I feel faint. Oh my word, the lift is creaking.

Mrs Peak Don't get it on my coat for goodness sake. It's real fur, you know.

Jackson Nor on my lift floor. Be careful.

Santa It won't stop.

Mr Peak It's clogging up his beard.

Cleaner It's all over his gloves.

Detective Exactly. I've caught him red handed.

Manager Well somebody *do* something. The sight of blood makes me feel all squiffy.

Amanda Just hold the bridge of your nose firmly. That will stop it.

Santa No – I have to have a cold object put down my back. That will stop it. That always does the trick – something hard and cold.

Old lady How about a coin?

Manager Or a frozen turkey? We've plenty of those in the food department.

Jackson A key? I've got a key.

Santa	Yes, that'll do the trick. [*He snatches it and drops it down his neck*]
Amanda	What a fuss about nothing.
Mrs Peak	Men!
Santa	Yes, it's stopped. It's done the trick.
Frederick	Stop moving. Keep still. Something groaned . . . .
Amanda	Ssshhh . . . . What was that noise?
Frederick	Probably the wire twanging – about to snap.
Manager	I say, Jackson, what's the largest number of people allowed in this lift?
Jackson	Nine, sir – so we're all right. There are only nine of you.
Cleaner	Just a minute – what about you as well? There are ten of us in a lift made for only nine. Blimey!
Frederick	We're over the limit – and all these parcels must be heavy. It's all extra weight on the wire. It'll stretch. The strain! We're probably hanging by just a thread – a mere twist of thin wire.
Mrs Peak	And Gordon's very overweight. It's bound to be an extra stress on the threads. I told

you to cut down on all that swiss roll and prune tart last night!

[*They all roll to the other side of the lift*]

Mr Peak   It's like that film where everyone got stuck in a lift.

Manager   Oh yes – I saw that – *Disaster on the Thirteenth Floor*. How did it end?

Mr Peak   Well they all got stuck for three days.

Mrs Peak   The sausage rolls will go off.

Cleaner   Then what happened?

Mr Peak   I can't remember.

Frederick   They were all killed – crushed to a pulp.

Amanda   Shut up! Keep calm!

Manager   Yes, whatever we do, we must keep calm. KEEP CALM!

[*All the lights go out*]

Cleaner   Aaah! A blackout – I can't see a thing.

Old lady   What fun.

Frederick   Perhaps we're all dead.

Detective   Right, hand over the diamonds, Santa.

Santa	Bah! Take the lot. I don't care anymore. I've given up. Just let me out of here.
Old lady	I hope my snakes haven't got out.
Jackson	Not in MY lift they don't. I can't see a thing.
Detective	Come on, Santa, hand all the bags back. Here you are everybody, grab your parcels.

[*They all grope*]

Mrs Peak	Ah at last, I've got my shopping back.
Mr Peak	I've got your perfume back – Happy Christmas, dear. You can have it now, just in case we don't see tomorrow.
Mrs Peak	I bet you haven't wrapped it up with nice paper.
Mr Peak	Well it hardly matters in here – it's pitch black!
Amanda	I've got my first aid kit back.
Cleaner	I've got my rat back.
Detective	I've got my secret papers back.
Manager	Thank goodness I've got my fivers back.
Old lady	And I've got the young man's roses back.

Santa	But that leaves three parcels still in my sack.
Detective	One is the missing diamonds.
Old lady	One is my snakes.
Jackson	So what's the other one?
Santa	Ha, ha, ha – the bomb!
All	THE BOMB?!
Santa	I'm not joking. I can still blow us all up if I want to.
Frederick	Amanda, listen to me....
Amanda	I've told you once, I've fallen for Rodney.
Manager	We could all be falling for Rodney in a minute....
Frederick	No, no, that film. I remember it now.
Amanda	This is no time to discuss the cinema. It's no good asking me out to the pictures now. I've told you....
Frederick	No – the hero in that film, he climbed out of the lift through the air vent in the top of the lift.
Old lady	Oooh, what fun! I'll give you a leg up!
Frederick	Me?

Jackson	Yes – there is a hatch, go on. You're the thinnest.
Frederick	Ooer.
Amanda	Well, Frederick, are you a man or a mouse?
Frederick	All right, then, I will – for you, Amanda!
	[*He starts to climb. All cheer but the lift rocks again*]
Mrs Peak	I never thought it would end like this.
Mr Peak	What?
Mrs Peak	My life. I only hope it's quick. It must be terrible to suffer for a long time.
Mr Peak	It is.
Mrs Peak	If I die, I want you to have my money and fur coat.
Mr Peak	But I'll be with you.
Mrs Peak	You can never do any thing right. It will probably end up at the Oxfam Shop.
Amanda	If I'd known today would be my last, I'd have worn my best dress.
Cleaner	If we do ... drop, sir, ... at least it will be good for trade. Look on the bright side.

Manager	How do you mean?
Cleaner	It'll be in all the papers. The January Sales will go like a bomb! We'd break all records.
Santa	That's not all it would break.
Detective	You fool. It's all your fault. Now hand back the diamonds before we all die.
Old lady	How about a sort of a hymn or something? In case we all ... die. Like the Last Rites. How does it go? "We are gathered here ...."
Amanda	I only know one hymn.
Detective	Then sing it. Anything to help.
Amanda	[*singing*] We plough the fields and scatter ....
Cleaner	[*singing*] Abide with me ... fast falls the ... creaking lift!
Manager	Try to think of a prayer or something.
Mrs Peak	[*singing*] Silent night, holy night, all is calm, all is bright ....
Mr Peak	Give us this day our daily bread ....
Cleaner	Lighten our darkness we beseech thee ....
Jackson	Even though I walk through the valley of the shadow of death ....

Santa	[*singing*] Twinkle, twinkle, little star . . . .
Old lady	In sickness and in health, till death do us part, as long as you both shall live . . . .
Detective	Come on, everyone – sing! How about "All Things Bright And Beautiful"?
All	[*singing*] All things bright and beautiful All creatures great and small All things wise and ooooeeerr! aaaaah!

[*They fall about*]

Frederick	[*in the distance*] Help! I'm hanging by a . . . .
Amanda	Fred! For goodness sake, TAKE CARE.
Cleaner	This is it, I know it. We'll all be crushed to a pulp. They'll never get to us on time.
Jackson	Of course! The phone. How silly of me. I can phone for help. There's an emergency cupboard in here with a phone in it.
Manager	Good thinking, Jackson. Open it up and dial away.
Jackson	Ah . . . but it's locked, sir.
Detective	Then unlock it and be quick about it. Time is running out.

Jackson	I can't – he's got the key. I put it down Santa's neck, remember?
Amanda	Give it back to him – QUICK . . . before we all fall.
Santa	Too late. I popped the key into one of the bags left in my sack. I don't know which one it was. It could be rather dangerous.
Amanda	I don't care. Please get it out. We must phone for help. Fred could fall at any moment.

[*There is a loud bang and flashes and all sway and scream. Then they cheer as the lights return.* Frederick *screams.*]

Amanda	Fred! Say something.
Frederick	Ouch!
Jackson	At least the lights are back. But he might never reach the emergency button at the next floor.
Amanda	Go on, Fred. Be brave. You can do it.
Frederick	I will, I will. Oh Amanda, I will . . . I hope!
Manager	Now about this key. How about it, Santa? If you choose the diamonds, I'll let you keep the lot and you'll be free. If you get the key, we'll all get out of here alive.

Mrs Peak	We could all go sky high if he sets off the bomb.
Santa	All right, all right – I'll do it. I'll play this game as long as I get to keep the diamonds.
Manager	If you pick the right bag!
Detective	Put all three bags in a row. As soon as you choose, you dive your hand straight into the bag and hunt for the key.
Old lady	I say – how thrilling!
Detective	Well, Santa – are you ready?
Amanda	I can't hear Fred. What if he slipped? Oh dear, it's all my stupid fault.
Santa	Very well – here I go. I'm going to shove my hand in the middle bag. Here goes ...
Old lady	What a scream!
Mrs Peak	Don't do it.
Jackson	Hold tight.
Manager	Brace yourselves.
Detective	This could be it.
Amanda	Frederick – speak to me.
Mr Peak	What a way to go.
Cleaner	I can't look.

[Santa *plunges his hand into the middle bag and pauses*]

Santa   Aaaaaah! [*He pulls out his hand, bleeding*]
          The pain – the blood!

Cleaner   He chose the snakes!

Old lady Oh dear – he's only got two minutes to
          live. What a shame and it's Christmas, too.

Jackson   But what about that key? It's our only
          hope. Aaaah!

[*Everyone rocks and sways*]

Jackson   We're moving! We're going up!

Amanda   Fred! Fred has done it – the hero!

Manager   What a relief.

Old lady I was just getting to enjoy myself.

Mrs Peak Think yourself lucky, Gordon.

Mr Peak   I always do, dear.

Cleaner   We seem to be juddering slightly.

Mrs Peak Something could snap at any moment.

Mr Peak   What a dreadful thought!

Jackson   No, it's all right – we're coming to the
          fourth floor.

Santa	Now look here. Here I am about to die and all you lot are worried about is getting to the fourth floor. Surely somebody's got some words of comfort as the doors open.
Jackson	Certainly. Fourth floor – children's toys, games and sweets. Santa's Grotto is closed for the moment because he's just about to die from a snake bite.
Detective	Well, Santa, you must admit I was too good for you. Take off that red hood and coat and beard. Show us what you really look like.
Santa	All right – it's all over now. [*He takes off hood*]
Amanda	It's you! Rodney, how could you do this?
Santa	I'm sorry, Amanda but I did it all for you. [*Doors open*]

Scene 14 Fourth floor

Frederick	[*standing outside doors*] I did it. I did it all for you!
Amanda	Oh Rodney . . . . Oh Frederick . . . . Oh, which one shall I choose?
Santa	It's got to be me – before I die. Hold me in your arms.

[*Pause as* Amanda *thinks*]

Frederick   Say something, Amanda!

Amanda   Oh Fred, I think you're wonderful. You'll be my hero for ever – come on!

[*They exit arm-in-arm*]

Santa   Now that's what I call sickening.

Mr Peak   Isn't love wonderful?

Mrs Peak   Shut up and help me with my shopping. We've got lots of things still to buy.

[*They exit*]

Santa   And what's going to happen to me?

Detective   Your two minutes must soon be up.

Old lady   I'll let you into a little secret. When the lights went out, I swapped my snake bag for the one with the roses in. You weren't bitten at all – you only stabbed your finger on a rose thorn. Clever, eh? [*Talking to snakes*] Come along dears, let's take you home. [*She exits singing 'Fangs for the Memory'*]

Santa   I don't believe it! I'm saved – I'm free!

Detective   I wouldn't say that. You're coming with

50

me. It's the inside of a cell for you this Christmas, but don't worry – we'll put tinsel on the bars, just for you!

[*The* Detective *takes* Santa *out*]

Manager   Well that's it then – back to work.

[*The* Manager *and the* Cleaner *move out of the lift onto the landing*]

Cleaner   After all the swapping about of parcels, which ones are left in the lift?

Manager   Simple. The diamonds ... the roses ... and the bomb ... I think.

Cleaner   That's if there ever was one. A bomb, I mean.

Manager   Good heavens, you could be right! It could have been a hoax.

Cleaner   And all that nonsense about the lift hanging by just a thin little thread of wire ... I ask you ha ha!

Manager   Ha ha yes, what a load of non ... I say, where's Jackson?

Cleaner   More to the point, where are the diamonds? The lift!

Manager   Gone! Nothing there – just a gap.

Cleaner	Just a wire hanging in mid air – frayed and dangling. It snapped – the lift's dropped!
Manager	Think of the cost.
Cleaner	Think of Jackson – he was in it – gone! He's plopped to the sewers below. Snatched from us in his prime.
Manager	Blimey! [*Peering down lift shaft*] What a way to go.
Cleaner	It's what he would have wanted. Like a captain, he's gone down with his ship . . . to the depths.
Manager	But I was about to give him a rise. I wanted him to be the new Father Christmas on the fourth floor. He was going to go up in the world.
Cleaner	Well he can't go much lower now. He's left this floor for the last time – faster than ever before. [*with hand on heart*] He was a fine man. Happy Christmas, Jackson, wherever you are.
Manager	We'll have him buried in the staff car park with the remains of his dear lift and on his grave stone, we'll have carved his final words . . . we'll even have them printed through the entire shop . . . on all prices in the January Sale . . .

Cleaner   [*head bowed*]   Going   down .... Going
              down ....

Afterword

In the rubble at the bottom of the lift shaft, there was no sign of
Jackson anywhere ... and funnily enough, the diamonds had gone too!
Both are doing very nicely, thank you – in the Bahamas!

Happy Christmas!

The Spirals Series

Stories

Jim Alderson
Crash in the Jungle
The Witch Princess

Jan Carew
Death Comes to the Circus
Footprints in the Sand

Barbara Catchpole
Laura Called
Nick

Susan Duberley
The Ring

Keith Fletcher and Susan Duberley
Nightmare Lake

John Goodwin
Dead-end Job
Ghost Train

Paul Groves
Not that I'm Work-shy

Marian Iseard
Loved To Death

Anita Jackson
The Actor
The Austin Seven
Bennet Manor
Dreams
The Ear
A Game of Life or Death
No Rent to Pay

Paul Jennings
Eye of Evil
Maggot

Margaret Loxton
The Dark Shadow

Patrick Nobes
Ghost Writer

David Orme
City of the Roborgs
The Haunted Asteroids

Kevin Philbin
Summer of the Werewolf

Bill Ridgway
Jack's Video

Julie Taylor
Spiders

John Townsend
Back on the Prowl
Beware of the Morris Minor
Fame and Fortune
Night Beast
SOS
A Minute to Kill
Snow Beast

Plays

Jan Carew
Computer Killer
No Entry
Time Loop

Julia Donaldson
Books and Crooks

John Godfrey
When I Count to Three

Paul Groves
Tell Me Where it Hurts

Barbara Mitchelhill
Punchlines
The Ramsbottoms at Home

John Townsend
A Bit of a Shambles
A Lot of Old Codswallop
Breaking the Ice
Cheer and Groan
Clogging the Works
Cowboys, Jelly and Custard
Hanging by a Fred
The Lighthouse Keeper's Secret
Making a Splash
Over and Out
Rocking the Boat
Spilling the Beans
Taking the Plunge

David Walke
The Good, the Bad and the Bungle
Package Holiday